Heroin Lies

by

Wayne Denfhy

Heroin Lies
by Wayne Denfhy

Author's acknowledgments:

For Jonathan and William.
Thanks to the students of Sir Harry Smith Community College, Whittlesey;
Harry Welch, R.A.F. Drug Prevention Officer.

First published by Cambridge University Press, Act Now series, 1991.
This new edition first published by **dbda** 2004. Reprinted 2005.

ISBN 1 902843 15 0

British Library Cataloguing in Publication Data
A catalogue record for this book is available from the British Library.

Enquiries regarding all rights associated with this play should be addressed to:
Wayne Denfhy, c/o **dbda**, Pin Point, Rosslyn Crescent, Harrow HA1 2SB.
Tel: 0870 333 7771   Email: info@dbda.co.uk (subject: Wayne Denfhy)

Further copies of this publication can be purchased from:
dbda, Pin Point, Rosslyn Crescent, Harrow HA1 2SB.
Tel: 0870 333 7771   Fax: 0870 333 7772   E-mail: info@dbda.co.uk

About the play

Vicki is an ordinary girl. She's no troublemaker or runaway, truant or secret smoker – well, not at first. She reckons she's reasonable looking, but isn't too keen on her ears, or her brother for that matter. She's got an untidy bedroom, loves music and boys, though there's nobody serious at the moment, and most of all she enjoys a good laugh with her mates. No, you can't really get away from it, Vicki is a very ordinary teenager and it's that that makes her story so frightening.

Heroin Lies is a sensitive and disturbing look at drugs and drug dependency, and in particular the pressures and influences at play on a teenage girl. We observe her gradual and tragic slide towards addiction and also the various degrees of help and hindrance she receives from family and friends.

Guided by a reporter and his nose for a 'good' story, we are slowly drawn into the world Vicki inhabits. It's a recognisable one, populated by real teenagers with real problems, misunderstandings and breakdowns in communication, arguments and laughter...

'And you always thought drugs happened to somebody else.' The fact that Vicki's tragedy could have been prevented is a warning to us all!

Go ahead!

'Read all about it! Read all about it!'

Characters

Vicki Brown	15, likable, class clown
Jean Brown	Vicki's mother, a worrier
David Brown	Vicki's father, 'head' of the family
Jason Brown	17, Vicki's brother
Jane	15, head girl, Vicki's best mate
Linda	16, the class stirrer
Michelle	15, Linda's sidekick
Wendy	15, everybody's favourite joke, manageress of the cafe
Mandy	15, the new girl
Mike	16, class poser
Colin	16, Mike's mate
Steven	16, Mike's mate
James	15, class wimp
Mrs Davies	Jane's mother
Headmaster	elderly pipe-smoker
Cafe assistant	
Reporter	narrator of Vicki's story
TV	off-stage voice

The original set

The play was originally devised as a Touring Theatre in education piece, the set for the original production being minimal. It consisted of a number of multi-purpose symbolic objects – a syringe, a bar of chocolate, a lipstick – that could be sat on or stood behind as required.

Stage directions

There are two kinds of directions in the playscript. Those in **bold type** provide information that is essential to an understanding of what is happening in the play at the time. For a play-reading, these should be read by a separate reader.

Those in *italic type* are less essential stage directions and offer suggestions to assist with a production of the play on stage. In a reading they are best not read out as they will hamper the flow of the play, although those who are reading may find that some of these instructions offer help with the interpretation of their lines.

Scene 1:   The saddest words

(Darkness. A heartbeat builds up then fades as the light comes up on Vicki's parents. Silence. They sit uncomfortably in a general hospital corridor. Both are lost in their own thoughts.)

David:
Do you want coffee? *(No reply)*
Always a funny smell in these places... corridors... miles and miles of corridors... why do you suppose they paint them white?

Jean:
Doctor said he'd be back in ten minutes, that was over half an hour ago...

David:
Can't stand waiting, hate it... queues... always seem to pick the wrong window...

Jean:
I just wish I knew what was happening!

David:
If they had some sort of system, it'd be something, but no...

Jean:
Can't be much longer.

David:
... just sit and wait...

Jean:
I wouldn't mind a drink or...

David:
If you're doing something, your mind can't wander, can't think. If only... my old man used to say they were the saddest words in the world.

Jean:
I feel guilty.

David:
(Angry) She knew what she was doing... if you're looking for somebody to blame...

(Jean is noticeably upset, David's anger subsides.)

It's just I'm a practical man... good with my hands... can't cope with feeling so useless...
kids look to good old dad to have a neat answer to every problem and I can't even...

Jean:
She's just lying there.

David:
Don't!

Jean:
I feel helpless... she looks so old... so tired... she's given up.

(Silence, footsteps echo in a distant corridor)
I was thinking... last time she was in here was when she had her appendix out... six, no seven years of age and for the life of us we couldn't stop her lifting up her dress and showing off her scar... sometimes to total strangers... oh, she was funny then and cheeky with it! Seems so long ago now...

David: Perhaps... er... I should get that coffee, now?... I'll be back... won't be long... OK?

(The reporter, who in the shadows has been watching the previous action, moves into the spotlight.)

Reporter: Read all about it! Read all about it! Tearful tale of a teenage junkie. This story's so hot, the foil's still warm... just like your favourite soap opera, but seedier, nastier, sadder... The real dirt behind the fingernails. This one will run and run... You'll cry till you stop. But I forget myself, ladies and gentlemen. This touching scene of grieving parents you see before you takes place during the tragic conclusion of our torrid tale. Let's start at the beginning... turn back the clock, something that poor Vicki could never do!

(Lights go down on parents. The reporter leads us to Vicki, sitting at her dressing table.)

Here she is, our front page news... to be continued on pages two, five, seven and nine, if blood sports weren't banned!... I know what you're saying... just an ordinary girl, nothing special. But watch her bleed at your leisure for pleasure, from your favourite armchair, in the safety of your own home!... And you always thought that drugs happened to somebody else!... Read all about it! Read all about it!

(The reporter fades into the background, Vicki 'comes to life'. She is pulling various faces in front of her mirror, each face slightly modifying her appearance.)

Scene 1

Vicki: It's me ears you see, too big, quick gust of wind and I'm up in the air, the Human Kite! Course you can do things with them nowadays, get them pined back like, I'm not sure if I'd be happy with that though, couldn't help thinking that when some hunk was tucking into me earlobe, something back there would snap and they'd spring forward, slapping the poor bloke across the face, like some SS officer... Suppose we've all got something about ourselves that we don't like, unless you bought your face off a Boots counter, like some girls I could mention, but I won't.

(She mouths 'Linda Johnson' to the audience, then continues putting on lipstick.)

Y'know, I sometimes wonder who I'm doing all this for, gettin' myself dolled up that is. I mean is it to make me feel better, or is it to attract some lad? I don't think that's why I do it, I'm not a tart. Nobody notices anyway, except me dad, and he only makes me wash it off!... I don't know if Mike'll notice. He's the latest love of my life. He's nothing special, but I just sort of like him. No more than I fancied the last one of course, but that's all part of the game, isn't it? I've got love all figured out, me, all I need now is the bloke. I wonder what the bloke I'm going to marry is doing now... right at this moment... Probably sitting on the bog... or with another woman!

(Laughing to herself she carries on with her make-up. Jason walks in. He obviously doesn't come in very often and is staring around her room.)

Vicki: Don't you knock?

Jason: What?... Oh sorry. *(Knocks on inside of door.)*

Vicki: Bit late now... What do you want?

Jason: Mum says tea's ready.

Vicki: Finished staring have you?

Jason:	Tell me, is that a boy or a girl? *(He points to a poster.)*
Vicki:	You should know the difference by now!
Jason:	Well it used to be that girls had longer hair, but now I'm not so sure! *(He notices some of Vicki's trousers.)* You don't wear these do you?
Vicki:	It's called taste, Jason. Something you just wouldn't understand.
Jason:	You won't be able to walk in them.
Vicki:	Well they're better than the flares you wear!
Jason:	Mum bought these!
Vicki:	It shows, looks like you're walking round on two hovercrafts! Cross your legs and somebody across the room gets their eyes poked out.
Jason:	Ha Ha... Very funny... I've just got more important things to spend my money on...
Vicki:	Action man needs a new costume does he?
	(Vicki continues with her make-up, Jason picks up some lipstick.)
Jason:	Why do you waste your money on this stuff?
Vicki:	Make myself look beautiful.
Jason:	Hasn't worked.
Vicki:	You'd look nice wearing make-up you know.
Jason:	Come off it!
Vicki:	No, straight up! Dab of blusher here, little dash of eye liner there.
	(Vicky collects some make-up and attacks Jason.)
	And a big puff of foundation!
	(They struggle amid screams and giggles. Mother enters. They stop instantly. Jason is covered.)

Scene 1

Jean:	What's all this noise then?
Vicki:	It's him.
Jason:	It's her, tell her!
Jean:	Quiet!! One at a time, now Jason… just look at the state of you…
Vicki:	But Mum!
Jean:	Jason will explain what happened.
Jason:	I was just sitting here minding my own business and this nutter attacked me with her make-up.
Vicki:	That's not right, he asked me to put it on.
Jean:	Is this true Jason?
Jason:	No.
Jean:	I think one Boy George is enough for this country to suffer. What would your father say if he knew his son wore make-up?
Jason:	But I don't.
Jean:	Well I've heard quite enough from both f you. It's time you started acting your age. get cleaned up, and get downstairs to that table, your tea's going cold!
Vicki:	But Mum, I said I didn't want any tea, I'm meeting Jane in a quarter of an hour.
Jean:	That's the first I've heard of it, young lady. No excuses, get downstairs and get that tea down you, or you won't be going anywhere… and that includes you too Jason!
	(Mother leaves. Jason is looking very thoughtful.)
Jason:	Vicki?
Vicki:	What?… If it's about the birds and bees, I haven't got time.
Jason:	No. It's not that… Vicki, who's Boy George?

Scene 2:   It's only a laugh

(The youth club. Disco lighting. Various characters are spread around the room in small groups. Wendy and James are the only two dancing. Jane is by herself waiting for Vicki. Vicki enters breathless.)

Vicki: Hi! Sorry I'm late, anything happening?

Jane: He's in!

Vicki: Where? Show us!

Jane: Over there!

Vicki: Where?

Jane: Over there! Behind you!
(She indicates towards Mike and his friends. Vicki begins to turn round. Jane grabs her.)
Don't look!

Vicki: How can I see without looking, idiot?

Jane: Pretend you've not seen him. We don't want him to think you fancy him!

Vicki: But I do!

Jane: Yes, but he's not to know that! Do you know your lipstick's on crooked?

Vicki: Is it? Damn! Me dad came in just as I was leaving the house. Made me wash it off again. Had to put it back on the bus. The driver didn't half keep giving some dirty looks... That better?

Jane: Yeah... Who's that with him?

Vicki: With who?

Jane: With Mike.

Vicki: You mean I'm allowed to look over there now, am I?

Jane: Yes, long as you do it subtly.

Vicki: Not like you then! Put your tongue back in...
Oh that's Steven.

Jane: Steven who?

Vicki: Davies... Dunn I'm not sure... went out with Linda

Scene 2

	Johnson for a bit.
Jane:	Probably got it, as well!
Vicki:	Jane!
Jane:	Well, you know what she's like, anything in trousers. No, I can see now he's not my type… Have to look elsewhere.
Vicki:	What's happened to Tim then?
Jane:	We're having a trial separation!
Vicki:	You mean you've finished?
Jane:	No…
Vicki:	Come off it!
Jane:	Well… Maybe… Anyway we're not here to discuss my love life!
Vicki:	Be a short evening if we were.
Jane:	Very funny… seen who's over there *(Jane motions towards Linda, Michelle and Mandy.)* Luscious Linda? Must be a full moon. God, she's got some nerve. Just look at the dress.
Vicki:	If my dog had a face like that, I'd shave its arse and walk it backwards.
Jane:	I think they've seen us *(Nudges Vicki)* Come on, put on your best smile. Wave back!
Vicki:	*(Through gritted teeth)* Silly cow!
	(Across the room, Linda and co. wave back.)
Linda:	Lucky escape that, thought for a minute they were coming over.
Michelle:	No danger of that. Vicki's too busy eyeing up Mike from over there.
Mandy:	Does she fancy him then?
Linda:	Can't you tell? She's got no chance of course… He goes for the more mature women!

Mandy:	Anybody we know?
Linda:	Put it this way, he's been rolling his eyes in this direction all night.
Michelle:	Hope you picked them up and rolled them back again.
Mandy:	Linda's trying to say, in her modest fashion, that he fancies her.
Michelle:	Didn't you snog him at Jane's party?
Linda:	Yeah, first time he kissed me... there was a burning sensation.
Michelle:	Don't tell me... he'd forgotten to take his fag out.
Linda:	You've got it in for me tonight, haven't you!
Michelle:	No... just kidding... Have you seen trendy Wendy's new man?
Mandy:	Bit of a horror, isn't he?
Michelle:	Reckon he's wearing that tie for a bet?
Linda:	They probably have cosy evenings by the fire, playing join the dots with each other's acne!
Mandy:	Go on, I dare you to chat him up.
Michelle:	I don't know... he's not much but he's all Wendy's got.
Mandy:	Go on... dare you!

(Jane and Vicki move across the room. Vicki dances behind James.)

Michelle:	I won't, but here's somebody who might!

(Mike, Steven and Colin are watching Vicki's antics.)

Mike:	So what did I do next then?
Steven:	Don't you remember?
Mike:	If I did I wouldn't be asking, would I?

Scene 2

Steven:	Well you bounded up those steps outside your house like they weren't there, and then you rang the bell with your forehead!
Colin:	Eventually your dad comes out, and you're still ringing the bell – you don't notice him...
Steven:	Even from where I was you could see your dad was going all sort of funny colours... blue... red...
Colin:	Then you finally noticed him... give him one of your big stupid grins and say 'Hello, Dad, I'm pissed.'
Steven:	And barge straight past him!
Colin:	His face was a picture, John was laughing so much he fell in the hedge!
Mike:	God, did I pay for it though... felt sick in the night, didn't I? I know, I think I'll throw up out of the window, nobody'll notice. Brilliant idea I thought... Seven o'clock next morning I'm woken up by my mother screaming 'Suppose you think that's funny, do you?' Forgotten there was a ledge outside me window, didn't I? Imagine it, all those blackbirds tucking into their second course of diced carrots. Me old man had a hairy fit, had me out there in me pyjamas spraying the roof with his old hose pipe! Never again!
Steven:	You always say that, until the next time.
Mike:	No this time I mean it... Do I remember something about me getting off with Linda?
Colin:	Yep.
Mike:	Oh God, I'll never live it down.
Steven:	What's that Vicki up to? *(They look towards Vicki messing about with James.)* Bit much isn't it? James is pretty harmless.
Colin:	Thought you fancied her?
Mike:	Did. She's alright to look at, bit of a child really.
Steven:	Shame, nice bum.

14

Colin:	Anyway, what did happen to that garden gnome?
	(Vicki is grabbing hold of James' trouser bottoms and shouting things back to her friends. Wendy is looking uncomfortable.)
James:	What are you doing?
Vicki:	Measuring the gap between the bottom of your trousers and your ankles mate.
James:	Oh…
Vicki:	There, finished… That didn't hurt, did it?
James:	No, quite enjoyed it really.
Vicki:	You dirty old man!
James:	You're Vicki, aren't you?
Vicki:	Right first time.
James:	I used to have a dog called Vicki.
Vicki:	You silver-tongued devil, you know how to charm the ladies, don't you. Have to watch him, Wendy, real ladies' man… How about us getting together then, James?
James:	Oh, I don't know. *(Looking at Wendy)*
Vicki:	Doesn't matter about her… C'mon, how about it?
James:	I… *(Wendy leaves.)*
Vicki:	That's settled then, down here, Wednesday. It's a date. *(Thumbs up to the girls)* See yer then. *(James exits.)*
	(Vicki returns to her group smiling. Mike is now with them.)
	It's all fixed up, then.
Michelle:	Vicki, you're terrible.
Jane:	I feel sorry for Wendy.
Vicki:	She'll get over it… it's only a laugh.
Jane:	I'm sure Wendy didn't think so.

Scene 2

Mandy:	You gonna meet him?
Vicki:	No... Oh, hello, Mike.
Mike:	Proud of yourself? 'bout time you did some growing up!
	(There is a silence. Vicki looks at her friends for help, then runs out of the club.)

Scene 3:   If you need a friend...

(Outside the club.)

James: WAIT WENDY!... I can explain.

Wendy: Go and explain to Vicki Brown... I'm sure she'll understand.

James: WENDY!!

(They pass Vicki in the shadows. The reporter steps into the spotlight.)

Reporter: Poor, poor Vicki. Enjoying yourself? No, don't feel bad about that. Funny isn't it how we gain pleasure from pain. Heard the one about the bloke who walked into a lamppost... see you're laughing already... Heard the one about the thick mick, the lazy black and the left-handed lesbian, you'll so hard it hurts!! Or there's the one about the girl who went too far, just wind her up and see her go. Poor Vicki, she's not begun to squirm yet. The man of her dreams thinks she's a kid and she knows he's not too far wrong. Ah, well, plenty more fish in the sea, at least she's got a shoulder to cry on.

(Jane comes out and puts her arm around Vicki.)

Jane: What are doing out here, it's freezing. Come on back in!

Vicki: NO!!

Jane: Oh, come on Vicki... he's not worth getting upset over.

Vicki: Nothing to do with him!

Jane: If it's not him, what is it? Come on, tell me, it's no use bottling it up, we all make fools of ourselves sometimes... Take me just yesterday...

Vicki: It's not just sometimes with me though, is it?

Jane: What do you mean?

Vicki: I'm always putting my foot in it and when that lot in there feel a little bored... it's let's set Vicki up time...

	she's game for a laugh an' like a fool, I can't resist the invitation. It seems that they're always laughing at me, not with me.
Jane:	Yeah, but you've got a choice.
Vicki:	Have I? It's alright for you being head girl... I wonder sometimes, if I stopped playing the fool... if anybody would notice me... Anyway, I didn't see you telling me not to.
Jane:	Yeah, well it was funny, but there are limits.
Vicki:	You're my friend, why didn't you stop me?
Jane:	Look, I'm not staying out here in the cold. Are you coming or not?
Vicki:	No.
Jane:	Oh, for God's sake Vicki!

(Jane goes. A few moments later Mandy comes out.)

Vicki:	What are you, the second babysitter shift?
Mandy:	Jane said you were a bit down.
Vicki:	Broadcast over the disco, was it?
Mandy:	Come on, give us a break. I know what it's like, starting new here like I did... there are times when it all gets on top of you.
Vicki:	I suppose we did give you a hard time.
Mandy:	I coped though. This stuff helped. *(Takes out a package.)*
Vicki:	Come off it, Mandy, I don't want any of that.
Mandy:	Are you even sure you know what it is before you start putting it down.
Vicki:	I know enough, enough to know I don't want it.
Mandy:	I don't know what sort of old wives' tales you've been listening to, but they're all lies. Go on, take it.

Do you want to feel like this again. Take some of this and you won't have to.

(She forces it into Vicki's pocket.)

Vicki: I don't know.

Mandy: Look, that's good stuff. I wouldn't give it to just anybody. Take it and if you need a friend sometime use it!

Vicki: If you were a real friend you wouldn't give me this in the first place.

(Vicki leaves... lights go down.)

Scene 4:   House like a hotel

(Vicki's house.)

Jean:	Vicki, is that you? *(Vicki enters.)* I could shake you... you've had me and your father worried sick... Where have you been all this time?
Vicki:	Walking.
Jean:	Walking? Is that it? You'd better give me some answers, girl, and quick !
Vicki:	No big deal, I've just been walking.
Jean:	Where to? Who with?
Vicki:	Oh, it doesn't matter, Mum, I'm home now alright!
Jean:	Alright, how can you be so cool... Do you have any idea where your father is at this moment?
Vicki:	A Soho strip club?
Jean:	I'm glad you find it amusing... for your information he's at the local police station.
Vicki:	Oh, Mum... Why?... Why make all this fuss... I've said I'm sorry... I just didn't feel like coming home straight away.
Jean:	You're treating this house like a hotel more and more every day.
Vicki:	Don't be like that!
Jean:	Didn't you spare us a thought while you were out gallivanting with your friends? Did you think about how we were feeling? No, no, I'm sure you didn't. Just typical, that. Me, me, me, all the time. You want to start thinking about other people for a change. *(A door slams.)* That sounds like your father back, I dread to think what sort of mood he's in!
David:	Oh, so you finally made it back then?
Vicki:	Dad, I was just going to bed.
David:	Sit down. You've got some explaining to do! Now where have you been?

Vicki:	I've just been telling mum this.
David:	Well you can just tell it again.
Jean:	She's been out walking.
David:	I think she can explain it for herself, dear… walking with who?
Vicki:	Jane, we just felt like walking.
Jean:	Didn't you think about the dangers? You read the papers like anybody else… It's so late…
David:	So you were walking with Jane?
Vicki:	Yes.
David:	Liar!
Vicki:	What do you mean?
David:	I've just been round Jane's house. She says you left early.
Vicki:	So that's it now is it, spying on me. What a big man spying on his own daughter. Don't you trust me or something?
David:	Seems we've just had cause not to.
Vicki:	Bet you never have to spy on wonderful Jason.
Jean:	That's not fair, Jason's got nothing to do with this!
Vicki:	He's got everything to do with it. Why can't you understand I'll never be like him, so stop comparing me. I can only say sorry so many times.
Jean:	But we do care, Vicki!
Vicki:	No you don't, I'm just a disappointment to you and I hate you for showing that. I hate you!

(Vicki leaves the room. Her parents look at each other, stunned.)

David:	I wonder what brought that on?

Scene 5:   The silent assasin

(The reporter steps from the shadows.)

Reporter: Dear, dear me! I know what you're saying. If she was my child. *(Sharp intake of breath.)* Nothing like your little angel of course, sat in front of Blue Peter as I speak, assembling a cruise missile out of yogurt cartons and sticky-back plastic. You can have them sitting there at your table chewing their meat forty-two times before swallowing, but unless that little bird sends back its messages you don't know what they'll do when they step out of your house... your castle... your prison.

Vicki planned her escape long ago, her little bird was stillborn. Are you sitting comfortably? Vicki discovered cigarettes, then the rot really set in!

(The reporter fades back into the darkness. Lights come up on a headmaster's study. There is a knock on the door.)

Head: Come in. *(Vicki enters.)* Ah, Victoria... take a seat! Now what can I do for you?

Vicki: You sent for me, sir.

Head: Oh yes, of course... er... I... a clue?

Vicki: Caught smoking, sir!

Head: Ah yes, tut, tut. Now, Victoria, I've been at this school now... oh, far too many years to remember... In fact I probably taught your parents... Yes, I'm certain I did. I often meet parents in the street, you know, and we laugh about the thrashings I gave them. They say Mr Graves, Mr Graves sir, they say, I remember that time you beat me senseless... it taught me a lesson, and nothing against these young teachers of today, but we respected you for that, sir. That's what they say, believe you me. The 'silent assassin', that's what they used to call me, on account of the fact that I used to creep up behind them, before braining them across the head! But the point of this, Victoria, and there is a point, a good point, I don't believe in beating around the bush, the point is, is that with all this experience behind me, I'm a past master at spotting somebody who is going off the rails. And that person is you, Victoria Brown. Truancy, smoking, and all in the last few months. Now hear this, you're a fit, healthy young lady. You go to a super school, have a thriving house system and you have parents who care for you. I...

Vicki: No, they don't.

Head: Pardon me?

Vicki: They don't care for me, they just care for my brother.

Head: Quite... er... don't be silly, of course they care for you, and as far as Jason goes, you wouldn't go far wrong by taking a leaf out of his book. Now I hope this little chat has been of some use, any problems don't be afraid to knock on my door... Right, well... run along then, child... I've things to do.

(Vicki leaves the room.)

Scene 6: The way you remember…

(Typewriter sound. Lights up on the Reporter, notebook in hand, and Mike, Steven and Colin. They are taking part in an interview. The reporter doesn't speak, but continually makes notes.)

Mike: Oh yeah, I remember Vicki Brown.

Steven: I mean, it doesn't surprise me!

Mike: She always was a bit strange.

Colin: *(To Mike)* Fancied you, for a start.

Mike: Very funny. No, I mean, she was y'know different.

Steven: Not one of the crowd.

Mike: Always seemed to be on her own, y'know.

Steven: Even when she was with other people!

Mike: Looking back, knowing what's happened since, like, I can see how it all started!

Colin: Bollocks!

Mike: What?

Colin: What you saying?

Mike: Things I remember.

Steven: That time at the Youth Club?

Mike: Yeah.

Steven: She was actin' odd that night.

Mike: Reckon she must have been on them even then!

Steven: Must have been!

Colin: What night?

Mike: Y'know, when she got off with James what's-his-name.

Steven: An'her an' Johnson had a fight over it!

Colin: Don't remember no scrap!

Mike: P'haps not a scrap then, but there was an argument!

Steven:	Anyway, why you being so funny?
Colin:	Well, it's like I can hardly remember anything… it was years ago, maybe the odd bit here an' there but you two, you, you've…
Steven:	Got better memories, eh?
Colin:	Too right… since this lot turned up, the way you go on you'd think she was your missus or something!
Mike:	So?
Colin:	So… so it don't seem right that's all.
Mike:	We're only telling the man what he wants to know.
Steven:	Yeah.
Colin:	P'haps, but p'haps the way you remember it isn't the way it was, an' I know I'd hate people telling tales about me if… if I couldn't answer back for myself!

(Lights fade, leaving the headline slide 'Troubled Teenager Tempted' illuminated. The Reporter closes his notebook. Blackout.)

Scene 7: Seeing a lot of her lately

(The sweet shop. Linda obviously works here. Michelle, Wendy and Jane are hanging round for the gossip.)

Michelle:	So what did he do next, then?
Linda:	That's my secret, and for you to dream about!
Jane:	That means nothing did happen.
Linda:	Oh, listen to the Old Ice Queen herself.
Wendy:	*(With the right accent and manner)* What was that, that Mae West woman used to say 'I was Snow White but I just sorta drifted.'

(They all laugh.)

Jane:	Wendy, I never knew you were like that!
Wendy:	Well, there's a lot of things you don't know, isn't there?
Linda:	Anyway, as I was saying, back to my love life. *(They all groan. That moment Vicki walks in.)*
Vicki:	Miss some joke?
Jane:	Not that you'd notice.
Linda:	What can I do for you, Vicki?
Vicki:	10 Marlboro?
Linda:	Not sure I can sell you them, not allowed you know, under age.
Vicki:	So that's not Chanel 'Benson and Hedges' I can smell wafting off you then, is it?
Linda:	Fair enough, here!
Jane:	Didn't know you smoked, Vicki?
Vicki:	Haven't long, can I have a word?
Jane:	Yeah.
Vicki:	I meant over here.
Jane:	You can say what you want in front of this lot.

Linda: We could do with a bit of juicy gossip.

Vicki: *(Whispering)* Look, I'd prefer it if didn't mention the smoking to my mum. She thinks I've given up, she'd only be upset.

Jane: I'm hardly likely to, am I? I've not been round yours for weeks.

Vicki: No… well, thanks anyway…

Linda: Look Vicki… A few of us are going on to a club tonight… fancy coming?

Vicki: No thanks.

Michelle: Suit yourself!

Jane: Where are you rushing to?

Vicki: I said I'd meet Mandy.

Jane: Seeing a lot of her lately.

Vicki: Yeah, well she's alright when you get to know her. Anyway, have to be off.

Linda: See you, Vicki. *(Vicki exits.)* Doesn't look well , does she?… Well, this bloke was telling me… what wonderful teeth I had.

Wendy: Like stars?

Linda: Not exactly.

Wendy: … they come out at night.

(They all look at Wendy, then burst out laughing.)

Scene 8: Take some… for me

(Vicki's front room. Jason is sitting watching pre-school TV. He's smiling.)

TV: And now children, we're going to be big strong trees… let's see you grow… come on you at the back there!

(Looking around the room, Jason begins to attempt the activity.)

Let's see those branches reaching out to the sky! Now that's not very tall is it?

(Jason jumps on to the settee to gain extra height. He looks very pleased with himself.)

That's better, now say hello to Mr Bird!

(The bell rings and he goes to pieces.)

Vicki: *(Offstage)* Jason, answer the door.

Jason: Get it yourself.

Vicki: *(Offstage)* It's Mandy.

Jason: Oh.

(He changes his opinion totally and goes to the mirror to check his appearance. When he's happy he opens the door.)

Mandy: Hello, is Vicki in?

Jason: Yes, she's still getting ready. You can come in and wait if you like.

Mandy: Thanks.

(They go to sit down. Jason's very much aware of her but can't think of anything to say.)

What are you watching, then?

Jason: Nothing much, kids stuff really.

Mandy: Oh, I don't know, I think they're quite cute, specially when they let out those little high pitched squeals, it's like they're getting over excited. Know what I mean?

Heroin Lies

Jason: *(Squeaking)* Yes!

Mandy: You're not really watching this are you?

Jason: No, just got it on for company.

(Mandy moves up the settee.)

Mandy: Good looking boy like you getting lonely?

(She puts her hand on his knee.)

Jason: Oh look, Tinky winky!

Mandy: Never mind the little handbag carrier, I'm interested in you. These are lovely trousers. They say jack ups are coming back in. Where did you get them?

Jason: I think my mum said Oxfam.

Mandy: Cardigan from there as well?

(Jason, sweating, moves further along the couch.)

Jason: Think so! Vicki doesn't like it, says it's like an old man's.

Mandy: What does she know?

Jason: That's what I say!

(They are now face to face.)

Mandy: Has anybody ever told you, you've got gorgeous eyes?

Jason: I think mum mentioned it once...

(Jason falls off the settee with Mandy on top of him. At this moment Vicki walks in.)

Vicki: What are you doing with my friends?

Jason: *(Getting up)* Nothing, nothing.

Vicki: Don't you tell me that, you filthy beast. I can't leave you alone for five minutes, can I?

Jason: I've got to... I've got to... *(He's already got his coat on.)* I've got to walk the dog.

Vicki: We haven't got a dog, Jason.

Scene 8

Jason:	Well, the cat needs a gallop then… Bye. *(He goes. Vicki and Mandy burst into giggles.)*
Vicki:	You shouldn't encourage him!
Mandy:	Oh, but he's sweet. Leave him alone…
Vicki:	I suppose so. What is it you want, then?
Mandy:	You know that night I gave you that stuff, have you still got it?
Vicki:	Yes, somewhere. I thought about using it once or twice but never did. Do you want me to fetch it?
Mandy:	If you could. I'm a bit desperate.
	(Vicki goes. We see a totally different Mandy – nervous. When Vicki comes in she grabs the package.)
Vicki:	No need to snatch.
	(Mandy gets out her lighter.)
Mandy:	Have you got a fiver?
Vicki:	A blue one, you must be joking. Me mam should have one in her holiday tin though.
Mandy:	Fetch it!
	(Vicki gets the note, offers it to Mandy.)
	Roll it for us.
	(Mandy starts to heat the heroin. Vicki starts to roll the note, then thinks better of it.)
Vicki:	Roll it yourself, I don't want to get involved… Do you have to do it here? Mandy!
	(She pushes Mandy. The powder spills onto the floor. Mandy turns and slaps Vicki across the face.)
Mandy:	You stupid bitch! look what you've done! Help me pick it up, You just don't understand, You don't realise how much this stuff costs… what I had to do to get it.

(After a short while she calms down. Vicki is still holding her face.)

I'm sorry I didn't mean to hit you... It's just...
I need it so much... things seem better... bearable.
Take some... I hurt you... feel better, let me help
you... please... take some... For me!

(As the drug is passed to Vicki the lights fade.)

Scene 9: Become a bit unreliable

(Outside in the street. Jane and Wendy are looking in windows. Linda and Michelle enter.)

Jane:	That one there!
Wendy:	The blue? Oh no.
Jane:	What's the matter, don't you think it'll suit me?
Wendy:	It's not that, it's just you always pick blue. Why do you always pick blue?
Michelle:	Matches her varicose veins, doesn't it!
Jane:	Hello, didn't see you there.
Linda:	Off anywhere interesting?
Jane:	Not really… just wandering.
Michelle:	Didn't see you at the party the other night.
Jane:	No,was it good?
Linda:	Great, got absolutely smashed, don't remember a thing.
Jane:	I was invited, but I decided to go out with Vicki instead. It was her 16th.
Linda:	She alright? Don't see much of her these days.
Wendy:	She didn't turn up!
Jane:	I'm sure she must have had a good reason.
Linda:	I'd heard she'd become a bit unreliable.
Michelle:	Not the only thing I'd heard. *(Linda nudges Michelle.)* What? I'm not saying anything wrong. Jane must know. She's a mate of hers.
Jane:	Know what?
Linda:	See I told you, big mouth… Nothing!
Jane:	No, come on… there's obviously something you're dying to tell me.
Linda:	No, it's not worth bothering about, really, probably no truth in it anyway.

Jane:	Well, let me be the judge of that!
Linda:	No, don't worry about it!
Jane:	C'mon tell me – you know you want to…
Linda:	OK, you asked for it, her and Mandy are on drugs.
Jane:	Oh, is that all!
Michelle:	What do you mean is that all? If she was one of my mates, I'd be pretty scared!
Jane:	You've been watching too many soaps. Vicki isn't on drugs.
Linda:	How can you be so sure?
Jane:	I know her too well, she just wouldn't.
Linda:	And all this faith comes from a friend she stands up. How touching!
Jane:	One thing I do know is that whatever the truth of the situation, she's not going to be helped by your dirty mouth, Johnson… Look to yourself that's what I say.
Linda:	What does that mean?
Jane:	You heard. Come on Wendy, I've got better things to do than stand here listening to this rubbish!

(Exit Jane and Wendy.)

Scene 10:   A real friend

(A quiet corner of the disco. Mandy and Vicki are sitting together. Jane enters.)

Mandy: Give us a light.. Ta, I still don't know why you wanted to come down here.

Vicki: I just did, remember that night I got upset over Mike... I was so stupid then.

Jane: Hello, Vicki.

Vicki: Hello.

Jane: Didn't expect to see you down here.

Vicki: Couldn't keep away.

Jane: Can I have a word?

Vicki: You've just had five.

Jane: No, I...

Mandy: I think she means in private... the looks I've been getting all evening you'd think I was the Wicked Witch of the West...

Vicki: You don't have to go.

Mandy: It's OK, I want another drink... Go ahead, Jane... She's all yours.

Vicki: Well?

Jane   It's just things I've been hearing.

Vicki: What sort of things?

Jane: Rumours, about you... Linda Johnson said...

Vicki: You've not started listening to her now, have you?

Jane: No... I've heard talk before she mentioned it.

Vicki: Mentioned What?... Don't keep me in suspense.

Jane: They're saying you're on drugs... and Mandy started you on them... Well, are you?

Vicki: A real friend shouldn't ask you those sort of questions.

Jane:	Yeah? And a real friend sticks up for you without knowing the truth… Say you're not, Vicki… PLEASE!
Vicki:	I'm not… I'm not… alright?… You've heard it from me now, OK?
Jane:	Yes… You understand… I had to ask… You know I did.
Vicki:	Yes… look, I'm sorry about the other night… my birthday… I just got tied up.
Jane:	With Mandy?
Vicki:	Yes, with Mandy as it happens… We'll have to make another date soon.
Jane:	Yes… Oh I nearly forgot. This is for you.

(She passes over a package. It's a silver bracelet.)

It's only something little, but I thought you'd like it. There's an inscription too.

Vicki:	*(Reads)* To my best friend… Jane.
Jane:	I had it done a long time ago.
Vicki:	Thanks, you staying for a drink?
Jane:	No, I've got to be in. Take care.
Vicki:	And you… and thanks.

(Exit Jane. Vicki is left looking at the bracelet. Fade.)

Scene 11:   Anything you like

(The sound of a typewriter. Lights up. Michelle enters, Linda is seated, the Reporter is barely visible in the shadows.)

Linda:	Is it in?
Michelle:	It's in.
Linda:	Can't wait, I've told them all at work... Well?
Michelle:	I don't think you'll like it.

(Michelle hands Linda a newspaper.)

Linda:	Give it here! What page is it on?
Michelle:	Page three!
Linda:	You're joking!
Michelle:	Best page for it, I reckon!
Linda:	I dunno what's wrong with you! It's not every day you get in the paper. *(She finds the page.)* What!!!
Michelle:	Bit of a shock, eh?
Linda:	Oh my God!
Michelle:	Well, say something!
Linda:	I... I don't understand... I mean... where did they get the photo from?... It's not the one he said he was going to put in!
Michelle:	No, you were showing a bit of leg in that one!
Linda:	Well, there didn't seem any harm in... but this!
Michelle:	I've been thinkin'... It must 'ave been that time you went in for Miss Wet T-shirt!
Linda:	I was drunk!
Michelle:	Looks like it!
Linda:	But they can't do this... can they? I mean what are people going to think?
Michelle:	What the reporter wants them I suppose!
Linda:	But it's years old... I don't look like that now... an'

anyway, what's it got to do with the story?

Michelle: The story?... Oh, yeah... I nearly forgot about that, have a read, go on...

(Linda looks at the paper. The Reporter steps out of the shadows to read the story.)

Reporter: Former Beauty Queen Linda Johnson, 27, told today of her teenage friendship with tragic Vicki Brown...

Linda: Seems fair enough!

Michelle: You came fourth in that competition!

Linda: I know!

Michelle: Well?

Linda: Why'd they put me age in?

Michelle: Dunno... always do.

(Linda continues to 'read' the paper.)

Reporter: 'We were friends' said a still attractive Linda 'the way only girls can be... if you know what I mean', she winked.

Linda: What the hell does that mean... she winked!

Michelle: Anything you like, I suppose!

Linda: I don't like it... makes me sound a right...

Reporter: Ex-model now spends her days a far cry from the catwalk; she can be found behind her local supermarket's checkout till. But she has no regrets. "I mean things could have been worse,' she gazed down at her shapely legs in sadness, 'Look what happened to poor Vicki'.

Linda: I've heard enough of this!... It's rubbish... I didn't say half of that...

Michelle: What did you say, then?

Linda: Can't rightly remember... but nothing like that... shouldn't be allowed.

Scene 11

Michelle: It's total lies, then!

Linda: Well... not really... but it's not the truth either... I tell yer, it's the last time I buy this rotten paper... Huh... 'Faded Glamour Queen'. I ask yer... disgustin'...
(Pause. Linda looks up smiling.)
Mind you... I don't look bad though, do I?

(The Reporter closes his notebook. Lights fade on headline, 'Faded Glamour Queen's Tragic Friendship'. Blackout.)

Scene 12:   Pay no attention

(Jane's home. Jane's mother is ironing, Jane is half-heartedly reading a girl's magazine.)

Mrs Davies: Your Auntie Mary rang up this morning, she asked after you. Asked if you were wearing your present.

Jane: What present was that?

Mrs Davies: You know, dear, that green jumper.

Jane: Oh no, that was awful.

Mrs Davies: Don't be so ungrateful... I'd like you to write a letter to her thanking her for it!

Jane: Oh, I can just see that. 'Dear Auntie Mary, thank you for the green jumper. It's what I've always wanted, it's smashing, people stop me in the street and say "Where did you get that jumper? It makes you look like a gigantic bogey on legs!"

Mrs Davies: Jane, really! (But laughs despite herself.) I suppose it is rather awful.

Jane: (Collecting her thoughts) Mam?

Mrs Davies: Yes, dear.

Jane: You used to have a special mate at school, didn't you?

Mrs Davies: Oh yes, Shirley Jones... great friends we were... don't know where she is now... last I heard she'd married some really dodgy character... Welsh I think he was!

Jane: If she was in trouble... would you help her out?

Mrs Davies: Of course... best I could... why, where's all this leading to?

Jane: Oh, nothing!

Mrs Davies: Come on, now you've started!

Jane: Well, there's been rumours about one of my friends.

Mrs Davies: Well stop right there... you don't get anywhere listening to rumours... the horrid inventions of idle tongues! Pay no attention.

Scene 12

Jane:	These rumours say my friend's on drugs. *(Silence)*
Mrs Davies:	Which particular friend is this?
Jane:	Vicki.
Mrs Davies:	Vicki... Jean Brown's girl? The one who used to be round here a lot... Well I never.
Jane:	If these rumours were true... how would you go about helping her?
Mrs Davies:	Do you think they're true?
Jane:	I'm not sure... Vicki says they're not and I would have believed her six months ago... but she's changed so much now... I can't tell.
Mrs Davies:	Well, my advice is to keep well away!
Jane:	But you said not to listen to rumours.
Mrs Davies:	Yes well, if there's only a grain of truth in these I don't want you to have anything to do with her.
Jane:	But how's that going to help her?
Mrs Davies:	As far as I'm concerned she got herself into this mess, so she can get herself out too. Keep well away!
Jane:	What if she can't help herself?
Mrs Davies:	I just don't want you involved... and another thing I don't want her round here again.
Jane:	You can't treat her like a leper, ignoring it's not going to make it go away. Just because you turn the TV off when those starving kids come on, doesn't mean they don't exist.
Mrs Davies:	Yes, but it means I don't have to look.
Jane:	That's horrible...
Mrs Davies:	These things are all self-inflicted... and that's the final word I want to hear on the matter... is that understood?
	(They sit in an uncomfortable silence.)

Scene 13:   Talk to me

(The Reporter steps from the shadows.)

Reporter: Click! *(He pretends to switch on a TV.)* I'm the man from the gutter press, and I've come to turn you on. Click! Hands up those who haven't crossed the road to avoid the dreaded Big Issue vendor. *(He looks round the audience.)* Liars! Click! You don't want famine when you're eating your tea. Click! Oh, look, it's a girl and I think she's drowning. Oh no, she's waving. I can see the silver bracelet and the track marks down her arm. Urgh. Click! This has been a party political broadcast on behalf of the apathy party. Click! Don't forget to switch off before you go to work. *(Laughing, he fades into the shadows.)*

(Lights come up on the library. Linda, Michelle, Vicki and Mandy are sitting round a table.)

Linda: Found any more dirty words in the dictionary?

Michelle: No, none that I can pronounce anyway.

Linda: God, this is boring.

Vicki: Can I copy your homework?

Linda: You could have, if I'd done it.

Vicki: Oh well… I made the effort.

Michelle: Procra… procras… procrastination.

Linda: Pardon?

Michelle: Procra… procras… I'm not saying it again.

Linda: Didn't sound as naughty as the last one, anyway… What was that again?

Michelle: I forgot. I'll never find it now… Stupidest things ever invented these. Use them to look up how to spell words and you gotta know how to spell the word to look it up.

Linda: That's the marvel of education for you!

Mandy: Don't look now, Vicki, but I think your second mum just walked in.

Scene 13

(Jane enters the room and throws something onto the table in front of Vicki. It's the silver bracelet.)

Jane: Recognise it, do you? Course you do, so you'll also know where I found it, won't you?

Linda: This some sort of 'Twenty Questions' is it?

Jane: You can shut up for a start, Johnson, you hypocrite. You've put so many knives in people's backs you could hang your entire wardrobe.
(They get up to leave.)
That's it – walk off. Don't like hearing the truth, do ya? How about you, Vicki? Fancy some truth? I'm still waiting for my answer.

Mandy: You don't have to justify yourself to her, Vicki. It's your life.

Jane: Oh yes, I forgot… your new chum… your special friend. I bet you even share the same syringe.

Mandy: Gosh, we have been reading up, haven't we? Miss 'Social Conscience'. What do you expect for this crusade, then? A little 'I Saved an Addict' badge for your Girl Guides uniform?

Jane: At least I never made one.

Vicki: Stop it! Stop talking about me as if I wasn't here. I've had enough of that off me parents… I don't need it off you.

Jane: Well, answer my question, then.

Vicki: OK… OK… So I sold it… Satisfied now? You said it was nothing much.

Jane: Obviously not.

Vicki: So I hurt you… I sold your special present. Sorry. Right, I've apologised. You keep it.

Jane: I don't want it.

Vicki: So you want me to have it? I'm putting it on… look… Happy? I'm wearing it.

Jane:	And you'll take it off again as soon as you need more money.
Mandy:	Put it round her neck and you could use it a lead... I've heard enough. Coming?

(Mandy exits.)

Vicki:	What do you want from me, Jane?
Jane:	Talk to me.
Vicki:	I'm talking to you now.
Jane:	Talk to me as if you mean it, like we used to. Why can't you look me in the face any more?
Vicki:	... It's not the same... I'm not the same.
Jane:	It can be like it was before... but the start's got to come from you. You were always the one with your feet on the ground... you would put me straight... make me see sense... I'm not doing this very well... but I'm asking you to put yourself straight, I want to help... if you'll let me. Just stop fooling yourself, Vicki... please.
Vicki:	You've always had faith in me... haven't you... I don't deserve it... can't live up to it... Don't measure me by your standards, Jane... I'll always fail. I'm not worth getting upset over... I'll be OK. Mandy and me have got this sorted now... wait and see... But don't get involved again, or I'll drag you down with me.

(Vicki gets up to leave, leaving Jane at the table.)

I was going to buy it back, you know.

Jane:	Yeah... 'course you were...

(Light fades. Jane is left by herself.)

Scene 14:   The right thing

(Typewrite sound. Lights up on the Reporter, sitting at a typewriter. David, Jean and Jason are in the shadows, a spotlight picking them out individually when they speak.)

Reporter:	I wonder?
Jason:	Done more...!
Jean:	... been stronger...
David:	... the right thing.
Reporter:	Where to appoint blame, that's the trick, pass the buck, point the finger... Ah *(typing)*, place the burden of guilt!
Jason:	She was my sister... I should have known... understood... told somebody... done more... our parents couldn't have know... But what could I do?... She wouldn't have listened... I was only her brother – anyway where could I go for help?... There's phone numbers an' that, but would you ring 'em? Would you know what to do?... It wasn't as if we were close... like we could talk of something... but just to stand and watch it was...
Reporter:	The coward's way out, new line!
Jean:	Try and start again... put it behind us... forget... but it isn't that easy... spent a long time hiding from the truth...
Reporter:	Truth hurts... no, too corny!
Jean:	You don't want to believe it could happen to your daughter... but you've still got to show her you care...
David:	... Teach her a lesson she'll never forget!
Jean:	You start lying to yourself... to others... strangers... that's what we were... strangers in our own home...
Reporter:	The headline!
Jean:	Sometimes... you forget... it's easier... Is it wrong I should feel that way?... If I could have been

stronger... for her... for us... but sometimes you
can be too strong.

David: I thought I did the right thing... I have to believe
that... Don't you see... if I stopped for a moment
to... to consider that I might have... y'know... how
could I live with myself. You can understand that...
can't you... can't you?

**(Flashbulbs go off continually in David, Jean and
Jason's faces. The typewriter sound starts and
gets louder. They slowly lift up one hand to
protect their faces. A typewriter bell rings.)**

Reporter: Print it!

**(Lights down. Headline slide illuminated
'Strangers in Our Own Home'. Blackout.)**

Scene 15: Trust 's no good

(Vicki's house. David and Jean are sitting down. david is playing with a small package.)

Jean:	But you don't know for certain, do you?
David:	This is proof enough… explains a lot of the things that have been happening round her lately.
Jean:	But it might not be hers… might be one of her friends.
David:	Are you blind, woman? Haven't you looked at her closely recently. I'm surprised she knows what day of the week it is.
Jean:	She's had a touch of flu, that's all… I don't think you shouting at her is going to help.
David:	Perhaps I've not shouted enough in the past.
Jean:	Can't we phone the doctor? Get some advice.
David:	Solve it all with a helpful leaflet… oh yes, I'm sure. I'm not having outsiders involved. This is a family problem and we'll solve it under this roof.
	(The door slams.)
	And I don't want you interfering with any of your soft ideas… There's only one way to sort this… Vicki, come here!
	(Vicki enters.)
	Going upstairs?
Vicki:	Yes.
David:	Well, you won't find them up there.
Vicki:	What do you mean?
David:	Your mother was doing her weekly tidy of your tip of a bedroom and she found this.
Vicki:	You've been through my things?
Jean:	They just sort of fell out… I'm sure there's some simple explanation.

David: Well?

Vicki: Well, what?

David: Do you deny this is yours?

Vicki: No. *(The parents look at each other in disbelief.)* What do you want me to do? Lie... I've had enough of lies.

David: Haven't you got anything to say?

Vicki: It's funny. From the first time I've always dreaded this moment... now it's here... I just feel sort of relieved.

Jean: How could you, Vicki?

Vicki: You'd be surprised how easy it is, mum.

David: I'm still having trouble taking this in... Aren't you ashamed? I know I am.

Vicki: I was at first, but after a while things like pride don't seem to matter.

David: And we're supposed to feel sorry.

Vicki: I... I...

David: Teenage pressures... that the excuse eh?

Vicki: I... get... confused.

Jean: I was young once.

Vicki: He wasn't!

David: I wasn't weak... you've been weak, girl.

Jean: David!

David: And I can't stand weakness.

Vicki: You don't understand...

Jean: We want to understand!

David: I understand well enough.

Jean: Listen... listen!

David: Had to be strong... for all of us.

Scene 15

Vicki:	Never asked you.
David:	I had no choice…
Jean:	When did you start?
Vicki:	Long time… too long ago… Mandy came round…
David:	Here!… You took them here?
Jean:	Better than the street…
David:	You brought that filth into my house.
Vicki:	In… in your chair.
Jean:	Vicki!
Vicki:	Under your nose…
Jean:	Vicki… it's no good…
Vicki:	Didn't have a clue… your chair… the same chair… I used to sit on your knee… You… you couldn't… why couldn't you see?
David:	*(Cold)* I trusted you.
Vicki:	Trust?… Trust's no good… Why?… Why couldn't you help me?… *(near to tears)* Why couldn't you help me?
David:	I'm going to make you regret the day you started.
Vicki:	Hit me… hit me, then… sure to make me stop… you don't care!
Jean:	We've always cared… <u>both</u> of us.
Vicki:	Never showed… he's not bothered… he's got Jason.
Jean:	I… don't understand.
Vicki:	Jason… Jason!
Jean:	Vicki, I…
Vicki:	Jason this an' Jason that… too many times.
Jean:	You're wrong… so…
David:	Jason would never do this.

Jean:	I can't believe this is happening... to our family... our daughter... must be some mistake.
David:	Proof you want is it?... I'll give you proof.
	(He grabs Vicki's arm and pulls back her sleeve.)
	Proof! Look... look... marks! Now can you believe, now can you see?
Jean:	Oh Vicki... Vicki.
	(She throws her arms around her daughter, Vicki's defence drops.)
Vicki:	I'm sorry, mam... I'm sorry.
Jean:	How you must have hurt... Well, everything will be alright now... Mummy's here.
David:	What?
	(David separates the two roughly.)
	I'm having no drug addict in my house... get out!
Jean:	David! This isn't the way.
David:	Get out!
Vicki:	I'm not stayin'... not in this shit-hole.
Jean:	David, please!
	(Jean stops David getting to Vicki. They struggle, she falls. Vicki goes to her.)
Vicki:	Mam!
	(David makes towards Vicki. She backs off.)
	Hit women, do you?... Fists instead of brain... God, I hate you.
David:	Just get out.
Vicki:	Remember... you made me what I am... think of that on the cold nights... you made me what I am.
	(She lams the door. David looks at Jean, then exits. Jason enters.)

Scene 15

Jason:	Mam?... Mam? *(No answer. He moves as if to go.)* I'll get dad.
Jean:	NO... No, leave him be.
Jason:	But...
Jean:	He's best left on his own... to think.

(Jason is staring.)

	Not... seen... me cry... too... often.
Jason:	No.
Jean:	Be alright in a minute.
Jason:	Does good to cry... you say...
Jean:	Shopping... I was going shopping... quick tidy 'fore I went... do no harm...
Jason:	Mam?
Jean:	Normal mornin'... like any other... never knew how a day could jump up an' turn on you.
Jason:	Mam...
Jean:	Few hours ago... smilin'... laughin' even..
Jason:	Mam... it's about Vicki, isn't it?
Jean:	You know?... Course you know... how long?
Jason:	A while... I...
Jean:	Why couldn't you tell us?
Jason:	Never, seemed the right moment... How can you tell someone... dad... something like that...
Jean:	You could try!
Jason:	I'm sorry.
Jean:	Don't.
Jason:	What's going to happen to her, Mam?
Jean:	I don't know... I didn't recognise her... the girl who was shouting... I had her there for a moment... but

David wouldn't let me... She had such anger in her eyes.... cornered... I don;t know if I'll ever see her again... isn't that awful?

Jason: Mam... I didn't hate her... you know that don't you?

Jean: I know.

Jason: Sometimes the way she went on she...

Jean: We all do things we don't mean...
(Silence)

Jason: Shall... I make a cup of tea?

Jean: *(Distant)* Oh... that would be nice... cup of tea solves everything... solves everything...

(Lights fade.)

Scene 16:   People we were meant to be

(Some time has passed since the previous scene. Mandy is sitting by herself in a cafe playing with some sugar.)

Cafe Assistant: You in here again?

Mandy: No law against it, is there?

Cafe Assistant: That's every day this week. Never seen anybody make one cup of coffee last so long.

Mandy: Must be a fascinating job if all you do all day is watch me drink. Need lots of qualifications to pour coffee, do you?

Cafe Assistant: Least I can afford to buy more than one cup. either you buy another or you get out. I'm fetching the manageress in a minute.

(She walks off.)

Mandy: So what? I'll fetch me dad.

(She checks through the change in her pocket, notices Vicki walking past the window. She tries to attract her attention. Vicki comes in.)

Vicki!... Vicki!... It's me, Mandy.

Vicki: Oh, hi, Mandy...

Mandy: Sit down... Haven't seen you for ages... What you doing nowadays.

Vicki: This 'n' that.

Mandy: Still living at home?

Vicki: Sort of... My mum keeps nagging me dad to let me go back... I do for a while, but he soon gets sick of me... Reckon if I was a horse, he'd have me put down. It's funny... Jason's been really sweet... keeps giving me bars of chocolate... read about it in some book somewhere... Can't stand chocolate... haven't the heart to tell him. What about you?

Mandy: Oh, doing great... got a job down London... just got back this afternoon. Reckon I'm gonna get promoted...

Vicki:	That's a nice story… something to write about… Might work for some old granny, but not for me. Don't take me for a fool, Mandy… I've lived with lies for too long… you just keep dreamin'. Got any stuff?
Mandy:	No… I thought you might.
Vicki:	And I thought you called me in to talk over old times.

(The manageress comes over.)

Wendy:	Excuse me, but I'm afraid you'll have to move along. We… hang on… aren't you Vicki Brown.
Vicki:	Might be…
Wendy:	Yes, you are. And you're Mandy Withnall. Don't you remember me, Wendy? You probably know me better as 'trendy Wendy'. I used to hate that name at the time, but it seems quite funny now. What are you girls doing nowadays?
Vicki:	We're government artists!
Wendy:	Eh?
Mandy:	Drawing the dole!
Wendy:	Oh, never mind. I'm manageress of this place, done very well, if I say so myself. Notice the ring. Go on… have a look. Got a little kid on the way, too.
Mandy:	Not James?
Wendy:	No. Gosh, no! I married Mike… Mike Peters. remember him. I'm sure you do, Vicki! You had a right crush on him at one time.
Vicki:	Did I?
Wendy:	Oh, yes! We're very happy… got a nice little house on the new estate, company car… can't complain… Anyway, it's been nice chatting to you, girls. we'll have to do it again sometime. Oh… and about the coffee… you have that one on me. What are friends for? That's what I say.

Scene 16

(She leaves.)

Mandy: Trendy Wendy... who'd have thought... Funny thing, your past... has a way of catching up with you... I don't think I like it...

Vicki: What ever happened to our lives, Mandy? The people we were meant to be... Dreams... such big dreams... going to do everything... be a singer... would sing out loud into the night... Met a famous singer once... forget her name... She gave me... a big, red balloon, I treasured it... kept it for weeks... till the wind tore it away... Tried to grab at it... was out of reach... nearly out of sight... it soared... I never stopped singing... not inside... so high... up... up... like smoke off silver foil.

(Lights fade to darkness.)

Scene 17:   Like tears

(The whole cast are assembled around Vicki in the darkness. Vicki's face is partly illuminated by a single spotlight.)

Vicki: *(A syringe in her hand)* Know what this is? Syringe... Doctors will tell you it puts things in... I know different... Takes stuff out... Don't let them fool you... That's full of pride... my pride... Have to look closely... not much left... like tears... see-through... willpower too... and love... Funny word 'love'... don't notice it till it's gone... My... my ... dad crossed the street the other day... rather than look at me... part of him's in there too... Mum doesn't go out much now... stares out of the window... all day... waiting for the phone to ring... worries a lot... about me... more than I do... about myself... Nobody's going to worry about me any more...

(She injects herself. From this moment on, we enter her drug illusion. All the words spoken by the cast will repeat. They will appear then disappear into the shadows. Vicki will often have to shout to make herself heard.)

Vicki: Won't be long now...

Jean: Come to mummy... Mummy will make it better... *(Repeat)*

Vicki: Mum... I'm... I'm sorry... I couldn't... I've let you down... I... I want... to be your little girl again...

(She reaches out to her mother, who turns her back.)

Jean: Vicki, how could you...? *(Repeat)*

Jason: Why do you waste your money on that stuff?

Vicki: I don't Jason, not any more... I'm going to get better... chocolate bars...

Mike: A real kid... 'bout time you did some growing up. *(Repeat)*

Vicki: Mike, I...

Scene 17

Jane:	You stood me up... *(Repeat)*
Vicki:	It... was... only... a joke.
Jane:	I'm sure Wendy didn't find it funny.
Wendy:	Snow White just sort of drifted... *(Repeat)*
Michelle	What did you do next? *(Repeat)*
Head:	Jason was such a good boy... *(Repeat)*
Vicki:	I don't want to be Jason... I want to be myself.
Jason:	Why do you waste your money on that stuff?
Vicki:	I'm... I'm not... make the world look beautiful.
Mandy:	When you need a friend, just use it... *(Repeat)*
Vicki:	Go away... Go away... I don't... I don't need... your sort... of friend.
Mandy:	Old wives' tales... take it. *(Repeat)*

(Vicki moves to take the drugs. Mandy hits her.)

Mandy:	You stupid bitch! *(Repeat)*
Jane:	I tried to help you, Vicki, but you wouldn't listen... (Repeat)
Vicki:	A real friend wouldn't... I tried... but... I... was always... too weak... Take me home, Jane... Take me home...

(She reaches for Jane. Mrs Davies appears and pulls her away.)

Mrs Davies	Keep well away... It's all self-inflicted... *(Repeat)*

(Vicki is on her knees. Her father comes out of the shadows, arms outstretched. She moves towards him.)

Vicki: Dad!... I knew you'd understand... You'd be there... when I really... needed you.

(She reaches her father. His expression changes.)

David: Get out! Get out!
(Repeat)

(Vicki falls to her father's feet. He continues shouting. The rest of the cast begin a mocking laugh.)

Vicki: Go away!... Get out of my head... I need... to be... alone... sometimes... please... Get out!

(The laughing suddenly stops. Then, very slowly at first, and almost whispered, the whole cast take up the playground chant of 'Vicki's on drugs'. They get louder and louder and more menacing. Vicki screams. Blackout.)

Scene 18:   Yesterday's news

(Single spotlight on Jane.)

Jane: They found Vicki unconscious... hunched over on
                        cold concrete.. in a phone box... amongst
                        yesterday's news and broken bottles... clutching her
                        bracelet... so tight... had to prise it from her...
                        changed the inscription with an old needle...
                        crossed out my name... scratched in 'Heroin'... She
                        died a few hours later... Think it was some sort of
                        message... I used to wear it myself until recently...
                        Then I had to sell it...

Writing the play

Who needs another play about drugs? I would have been inclined to agree with that viewpoint up until a couple of years ago. That was before a series of drug-related drama lessons with my G.C.S.E. group.

Although there had been blanket media coverage on the drugs problem, it seemed that rather than help us understand drugs more, it had merely created new stereotypes. The shady anonymous pusher, the drug-taking under bridges or in derelict houses and the way that drug-taking seemed to be a purely male-based activity, all these half-truths only obscured the most important question, why? Why is it that some children take drugs? It's that question that is central to this updated edition of *Heroin Lies*. Since the original publication the problem has refused to go away and in many ways has got worse.

Drug abuse is a strange sort of topic: everybody seems to think that they know something about it – it nags away at our national consciousness and titillates us in the national press. Sadly, there's a sort of dark romanticism attached to it, passed on by countless generations of dead rock-stars, and yet the most frightening thing of all remains the disturbing attitude amongst the general public that drugs, like plane crashes, happen to somebody else.

It takes only a little research to reveal the truth: according to a report from the Department of Health, 22% of 15 to 18 year olds have tried class A drugs, four out of ten 15 year olds have taken at least one drug in the last year. 300,000 children live in a home where at least one parent or carer has a serious drug problem. The majority of users obtain their drugs initially from friends and often take them at home. It was important for us that *Heroin Lies* reflect our findings. Vicki had to be ordinary, somebody the audiences could relate to; and the fact that nobody fully understands the causes of addictive behaviour surely means that every child is potentially at risk.

Wayne Denfhy

Heroin lies – See a friend in tears

Words: W. Denfhy   Music: B. Vafidis

Walking barefoot on broken glass
Clouds pass over a watching moon
A telephone box with empty windows
A broken mouthpiece, a waiting queue
A tattered book of distant numbers
Missing pages of a previous life
A final glance in a shattered mirror
Just above where Vicki carved out Mike

Chorus: *Heroin lies – See a friend in tears*

A number's dialled, hearts still pounding
Hung up when you hear her speak
A mother's voice brings childish memories
You've left the family album incomplete
A mother's tears and a father's anger
Never understands but accepts the blame
A final glance from a frightened neighbour
A mother's loss become a gossip's gain

Chorus: *Heroin lies – See a friend in tears*

Thoughts of Mandy's smiling eyes
And her pockets packed with hate
Hate that led to this phonebox floor
A shivering world you can't relate
Receiver swings in the dead of night
Pale, perhaps you've stopped breathing
A final glance at shattered life
Just above which Vicki carved out heroin

Chorus: *Heroin lies – See a friend in tears*

Follow-up activities

By Peter Rowlands

Note: The end section of this play quite intentionally deals with the underlying issues of behaviours and attitudes that surround the issue of drug use. It was thought inappropriate to use direct address on the effects and deprivations of drug use: educational research suggests that confrontational or shocking approaches are not effective in approaching the problem.

Discussion

Vicki, the central character in *Heroin Lies*, meets her death through the abuse of heroin. It is a tragic and pessimistic story which as Wayne Denfhy, the playwright, says in the section 'Writing the play', reflects what can happen to young people who find themselves mixed up in the terrible world of drug-taking. The fact is that we all take drugs of some kind or another at some time in our lives. More often than not we do so for very positive reasons. There can be few of us in the Western world who have not benefited from medicine and remedies that are drug-based. Many of us use drugs socially, drugs such as alcohol, tea and coffee. We may live out long lives without experiencing any really detrimental effects from their use. Often, using such substances makes us feel good in ourselves even though we know that they are destructive for out bodies. One of the most damaging drugs that is used widely, and that is readily available in the corner shop, is tobacco. Each year, thousands of people suffer the pain and indignity of smoking-related diseases, which disable and sometimes kill. The abuse of alcohol is a problem because it cannot only disfigure the life of the person who drinks too heavily but can have real costs for their families and friends. When mixed with driving, drinking may kill or maim others. Prescription drugs can be abused too, and you have probably read, or maybe know, of people whose lives have become dependent on various drugs.

It is easy to make judgements of other people. Most of us are too quick to say 'It could never happen to me.' And yet it could. The most important lesson to take from *Heroin Lies* and the debate about drug abuse may be that we need to learn to be responsible for our lives and happiness. Vicki suffers from a terrible self-image. She describes herself as a 'human kite' because her ears are so big. She feels abandoned

Follow-up activities

and uncared for by her family. She is sensitive to being called a 'kid'. Research suggests that nearly all drug abuse, such as smoking or heavy drinking, is related to poor self-image.

The following section offers a number of discussion points around some of the issues in the play. It is probably best to talk about the issues in small groups. One thing to remember is that what you talk about is serious and often personal. Each and every group member needs to be aware of his or her responsibility for taking the issues seriously by listening carefully and sympathetically to what everyone has to say. You also have the right to be heard in the same careful and sympathetic manner.

Task 1

On page 12 Vicki makes a remark about someone she is trying to put down and says, 'If my dog had a face like that, I'd shave its arse and walk it backwards.' The exchanges between Vicki and her friends are often like this – smart and sarcastic.

- Why do you think Vicki does this?
- What does it do to other people?
- How does it make her look in the eyes of her friends and feel within herself?
- Are you aware of the times that you do similar things?
- What makes you do them?
- Are your reasons the same as others in the group?
- Is it easy for people to pay compliments to other people?
- How do you feel when someone pays you a compliment?
- What does it feel like to be put down?

Task 2

Before beginning the discussion, draw up two columns on a sheet of paper and make a list on one side of all the things that make you feel good or 'high'. Examples could be things like buying new clothes and being smart or fashionable, winning at a game, going for a long walk by yourself, having a bath. In the other column, list the things that make you feel bad or 'low'. Maybe they'll be things like wet days, too much homework, nothing on TV or, yet again, having a bath. When you've done this, share the different lists with members of your group.

Heroin Lies

- Does anyone have a 'high' that you call a 'low'?
- Why do you feel differently about the same thing?
- Are there people in your group who enjoy the same things but do so for quite different reasons?

Once you've talked about this for a while, spend some time considering Vicki's life.

- What things made her feel high or low?
- What did smoking and heroin do for her self-image?
- Why do you think she used these drugs?
- In what way could she perhaps have avoided becoming involved?
- What high or good things could she have done to make her feel better about herself as a person?

Task 3

On page 34 Vicki is asked by Jane whether the rumours about her taking drugs are true. Vicki replies, 'A real friend shouldn't ask you those sort of questions.'

- Do you think Vicki is right?
- Do you think Jane was right to ask?
- What other ways may there have been of approaching the problem?

The group may like to think about other negative situations people find themselves involved in and whether we have a right to ask questions.

- What is the difference between being concerned and being nosy?

Task 4

If you have had the time to involve yourself in the questions raised above, you may like to undertake the following discussion as a whole class.

- How could Vicki's fate have been avoided?
- In what way could she have taken responsibility for her happiness and well-being?
- What contributions could other people have made to support her in her day-to-day living?
- How responsible are Mandy and Jane for what happened in Vicki's life?

Follow-up activities

Project

Alcohol, cigarettes and coffee are widely advertised in magazines, on billboards and in the cinema. Alcohol and coffee are also advertised on television. Spend a week noting examples of this sort of advertising and working out roughly what percentage of all the advertising you see is made up of alcohol, smoking and coffee adverts.

Task

Select one particular social drug such as alcohol and collect as much advertising material as you can. You may even have access to a video-recorder, in which case you could record advertisements from the television in order to study them.

Take a close look at how the products are advertised. Some may have a narrative, or story, attached to them. In some instances the story can be quite complex and be part of an advertising campaign that lasts a very long time (years in the case of one instant coffee). Other advertising may lend glamour or status or fun to the product.

- If people are involved in the images, what sort of people are they?
- How do they fit into the world that you know and experience every day?
- What other images/objects are included in the advertisements and what do they suggest?
- A car could be an example and, if so, is it like the rusting saloon that regularly parks outside your house?
- Are the interiors of homes similar to the one you are constantly nagged about for leaving untidy?
- Is the workplace similar to those your friends work at?

Sometimes one advert (text) relies on you knowing about another advert (text) for its effect, often a previous advert promoting the same product. This is known as 'inter-textuality'. An advertising campaign of this sort expects you to pick up on a specific colour, a story-line or a scene which is repeated over a series of adverts. An example would be the use of colour in adverts for some well-known brand of cigarette. There is always a line at the bottom of these adverts carrying a government health warning, but this is the only way the adverts make clear what sort of product they're actually promoting.

- Are any of the adverts you chose funny?
- If so, how does the humour work?
- Does the humour have everything to do with the product at all?

Having spent some time studying and analysing your area of advertising, see if you can make up your own advertisement using similar techniques to give quite a different message. The meaning that you want to get across to your audience is to warn them that the product has negative effects on lives, or that there are other ways of finding relaxation or a positive feeling about yourself. Try not to make the advertisement seem moralistic, or threatening and full of gloom, but attempt to use glamour, a story-line, humour, or references to other advertisements (inter-textuality) to get your message across.

If you are using a single image in a printed form, you could cut up images and paste them onto a large sheet of paper in a new combination to give you a collage of your fresh advertisement. If you have been looking at television advertising, make up a story-board so that each moment of the advertisement is a still image, much as in a comic. If you have been listening to radio advertising, you could record your advertisement onto a cassette tape.

Follow-up activities

Writing tasks

When we talk of drug abuse, we often use the words addiction, habit and dependence. It is worth thinking about these words for a moment and deciding what the difference is between them. Is a habit the same as dependence and is dependence necessarily an addiction? You may have a habit of biting your nails. Is this also dependence? You may depend on the bus routes and timetables that service your street. Is waiting for the bus an addiction?

We are dependent in our lives on a great many things other than drugs. The dependence is not always one that everyone shares. Some people cannot sleep in a room without a bedside lamp on. We can become addicted psychologically to things like eating chocolate, but this is not the same as a physiological dependence on heroin or nicotine, which alters the way the body works. We can have good habits such as being tidy or kind and bad habits like being dirty and rude. Human life is also full of strange and quirky behaviours that make us feel better about ourselves without damaging our health or affecting the quality of other people's lives.

Task 1

Write a brief story about someone's dependence upon something in their lives which for other people looks odd but, for the person concerned, makes them feel positive and happy. It could be an old lady and her dependence on a loved but mangy cat. It could be a child with a favourite toy. Try, in your writing, to give two points of view: the point of view of the person with the dependence and how it makes him/her feel about his/her daily life and routine; and the point of view of someone else who makes a judgement about the dependence.

Task 2

We all have habits. Some we like and some we hate. Some of our habits other people hate. Have you ever sat next to someone in the cinema who spent their time cracking their knuckles all the way through a really good film?

Write a letter to an imaginary friend who has a habit that you hate, explaining why you don't like this particular behaviour, and suggest ways of stopping the habit. Try and make the letter really supportive and sympathetic rather than a put-down. Remember that habits can have side effects such as stumpy, chewed nails, that aren't attractive. Would a nail-chewing friend feel much better about her/himself if their hands were attractive?

When people come off drugs for after a period of high dependence, it is called withdrawal. This withdrawal can be very painful. The side effects of withdrawal from alcohol are known as the 'DTs' or delirium tremens. It is agonising and can involve physical convulsions and sweats accompanied by horrible hallucinations. When withdrawing from drugs, the experience is known as 'cold turkey' and has very similar consequences. Even giving up smoking can be quite physically distressing. Alongside the breaking of dependence is the loss of a habit. Smokers very often smoke at particular times of the day or after doing certain things. Suddenly these times can seem odd and difficult without the habit. The person may go through a kind of grieving at the loss of something that gave their day some meaning. You may have given up a habit and had much the same feelings of being a bit lost – as if things weren't quite right.

Task 3

Choose a habit, either imaginary or real, and write out a plan of a typical day and how that habit fits into all the things that happen. For example:

7.00 a.m.   Wake up. Reach for cigarettes. Quick fag before going to bathroom for morning cough and wash.

7.20 a.m.   Downstairs for breakfast of black coffee and a cigarette... and so on.

Having done this, work out a programme for the same day in which the only thing that is missing is the habit. Everywhere that the habit existed, find something positive to replace it with. The positive thing must change during the course of the day, otherwise you will just be replacing one habit with another!

Task 4

Write a letter to a friend describing the loss of a friend who has moved to another town. This person was very special to you and you were in the habit of spending large amounts of time together and would jointly do all sorts of things quite regularly. You had got into a habit with one another. Now this friend has gone, your days have become quite different. Describe the days before and after the move, and the loss of this friend. Explain how the future may work out and how you will spend your spare time now. Importantly, write about your feelings.

Follow-up activities

Drama ideas

The following ideas for practical drama are only a few approaches to exploring the themes and ideas in *Heroin Lies*. Really good drama tends to come from the ideas that you have thought of for yourselves, and it may be that sitting down and exploring with one another the issues raised by the play may throw up some things that you want to turn into a practical drama piece.

Idea 1

In Scene 6, Mike Steven and Colin are portrayed as adult and are interviewed by a reporter. How they remember events involving Vicki and how these events actually happened are a bit different. You have probably heard similar conversations, in which a little bit of exaggeration has spiced up what actually took place.

With a partner, (i) work out a quick scene which involves one person tempting the other into taking up smoking; and (ii) work out a second scene, where the person being tempted to smoke in the first scene becomes a teacher interviewing the tempter. Can the tempter twist the truth so that they aren't actually lying about trying to make a friend smoke, yet not quite telling the truth?

Idea 2

In Scene 8, Vicki has difficulty in saying a straight no to Mandy when she tempts her with the heroin that has been hidden in the house. In the end Vicki is persuaded by the argument that she should 'take some... For me!' In what other ways could this have been handled by Vicki? With a partner, take the roles of Vicki and Mandy and see if you can rework the scene so that Vicki can be positive and assertive and say 'No' and mean what is said. The person playing Mandy should try every tactic possible to persuade Vicki that she ought to try the drug.

Idea 3

Scene 11 finds Linda and Michelle reading a newspaper report of Linda's friendship with Vicki in which the reporter manages to twist meanings and insinuate things by the way in which he writes.

Work out a group scene involving Vicki and her family discussing her drug dependence. Following this, choose one person to represent the scene by being a reporter giving a spoken television report of what happened in the home. You may wish to show the report to an audience and ask them to guess at the reality before showing them the group scene. Remember, the reporter is unlikely to actually lie. Just stress a few things and sensationalise the issue.

Idea 4

In Scene 15, towards the end, there is a conversation between Jason and his mother about Vicki and her drug problem. It is revealed that Jason knew about the heroin and was unable to tell his parents. We quite often feel frightened about telling people a particular piece of news. Sometimes this is to protect them. Sometimes to protect ourselves. It is a very understandable state of affairs but sometimes it is important that the news is broken, so that help can be given.

In a small group, experiment with ways in which Vicki's parents could be told of Vicki's drug problem. Be aware, as you work on this scene, of the feelings of each member of the family.

Idea 5

Often, when someone attempts to suggest to us that something we are doing is wrong, dangerous or harmful, we are tempted to reply that it is our right because it is our life and our risk. But is this always true? Is it just Vicki who is affected by the heroin dependence that she becomes involved with? In the following simulation the issue is whether motorcyclists have the right to decide to ride a motorbike without a crash helmet. Each member of the group should take up one of the suggested roles and then work on the group scenes suggested.

Michael Levine	Young motorcyclist enthusiast. Doesn't believe in wearing a rash helmet.
Sharon Doran	Going out with Michael. Continually suggesting that Michael should wear a helmet.
Betty and Bill Levine	Michael's parents.
Garth Aller	A motorist. Suffers from a heart problem.
Bobby Waites	A patient waiting for a bed in a men's surgical ward for an operation on his hip.

Follow-up activities

Linda Waites	Married to Bob. Nursing her husband at home.
Charge Nurse Marsh	Nurse in charge of men's surgical ward.
Ambulance man	
PC Forte	A policeman.

- Work on a scene between Michael and Sharon about Michael's continual breaking of the law and wearing a crash helmet. Why does Michael insist on doing this? Why does Sharon object?

- Explore the scene in which Michael has an accident on the road in which he has taken a corner too wide and met head on with a car driven by Garth Aller. Michael is very seriously injured. The police constable arrives on the scene and tells Garth that he is likely to be charged because, although he didn't cause the accident, his tyre treads are too thin. The ambulance man tells everyone that Michael is unlikely to live because of serious head injuries.

- A brief scene between Michael's parents and Sharon in which they are told by Nurse Marsh that Michael is unlikely to live.

- A scene where Bobby Waites arrives for an operation on his hip, which has been booked for six months, to be told that the bed is no longer available because Michael has taken his place. Linda Waites is with him and due to take several days' break with her sister because she is exhausted and run down.

- Michael recovers after all. Everyone in the group should maintain their roles and meet in a circle to discuss the effect on their lives of Michael's crash and his head injuries.

Following this short simulation you might like to discuss the issues that have been raised and how they might apply to Vicki or to any of us who make decisions that put other people's happiness at risk. When are such decisions right? When are they wrong?

Useful contacts

If you wish to look into the issue of drugs and drug dependency in more detail, or if you need any form of support or advice, the following contacts may be of help.

- **Addaction** (help in managing effects of drug/alcohol misuse)
  Tel: 020 7251 5860
  www.addaction.org.uk

- **ADFAM** (Families, drugs and alcohol)
  Tel: 020 7928 8898
  www.adfam.org.uk

- **Drug Concern** (parent and family support)
  Helpline: 0845 120 3745

- **DrugScope** (expert advice on drugs)
  www.drugscope.org.uk

- **Families Anonymous** (support for families and friends)
  Helpline: 0845 120 0660   Faxline: 020 7498 1990
  www.famanon.org.uk

- **National Drugs Helpline**
  Tel: 0800 776600
  www.talktofrank.com

- **Parents Against Drug Abuse (PADA)** (support for parents of drug users)
  Helpline: 0845 702 3867
  www.btinternet.com/padahelp

- **Release** (health, welfare, legal needs of drug users and families – specific advice, support, information for heroin users/carers)
  www.release.org.uk

- **The Centre for Recovery** (info and advice – special section for teenagers and parents)
  www.recovery.org.uk

- **Wotz da factz** (drug awareness for young people)
  www.wotzdafactz.co.uk

Other plays published by *dbda*

If you have enjoyed reading and/or working with this playscript, you may like to find out about other plays we publish. There are brief descriptions and other details on the following pages.

All plays deal with contemporary social and moral issues and are suitable for Youth Theatres, Schools, Colleges, and adult AmDram. They are ideal for GCSE Drama/English exam use and frequently do well in One Act Play Festivals. They offer both male and female performers equally challenging opportunities.

For enquiries or to order plays published by *dbda*, please contact:
dbda, Pin Point, Rosslyn Crescent, Harrow HA1 2SB.
Tel: 0870 333 7771
Fax: 0870 333 7772
Email: info@dbda.co.uk

All enquiries regarding performing rights of 'Heroin Lies' by *Wayne Denfhy*, should be made to:
Wayne Denfhy, c/o *dbda*,
Pin Point, Rosslyn Crescent, Harrow HA1 2SB.
Tel: 0870 333 7771
Email: info@dbda.co.uk (subject: Wayne Denfhy)

All enquiries regarding performing rights of plays by *Mark Wheeller*, should be made to:
Sophie Gorel Barnes, MBA Literary Agents,
62 Grafton Way, London W1P 5LD.
Tel: 020 7387 2076
Email: sophie@mbalit.co.uk

All enquiries regarding performing rights of 'Gagging For It' by *Danny Sturrock*, should be made to:
Danny Sturrock, c/o *dbda*,
Pin Point, Rosslyn Crescent, Harrow HA1 2SB.
Tel: 0870 333 7771
Email: info@dbda.co.uk (subject: Danny Sturrock)

Other plays published by *dbda*

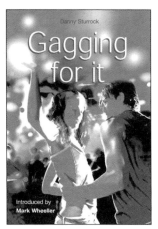

NEW – Gagging for it by Danny Sturrock

Summer is here, A-levels are over and a group of 6 friends embark on a holiday to Ibiza! What would their holiday bring? Would Chris finally pluck up the courage to ask out Teresa? Would Jay drink himself into oblivion? Would Bianca spend the entire holiday flirting with the Spanish barmen – more than likely! ...or would a chance encounter with an old friend bring their hedonistic worlds crashing down around them!?

Comedy, dance music and choreography are the keys to this production. The pace is breakneck and hilarious, but once the party's over, it hits you!

ISBN 1 902843 17 1

Cast: *3f, 3m &3m/f or 3m & 3f for GCSE using suggested cuts*
Duration: *55 minutes approx.*
KS 3 & 4

'Really funny... laugh out loud funny. Inspired outstanding performances from the six Year 11s who went on to exceed our expectations by a long way in their GCSEs achieving A or A*. It proved to be a firm favourite with our KS3/4 audience.

Mark Wheeller

NEW – Legal Weapon II by Mark Wheeller

This is a new "improved" version of the popular Legal Weapon play which, from summer 2005, will go out on tour to schools across the UK.

Legal Weapon told the story of a young man's relationship with his girlfriend, Jazz, and his car. Both are flawed, but his speeding causes the loss of a life and the loss of his freedom.

In Legal Weapon II Andy has to reveal to Jazz that he has killed someone very close to her... her best friend!

Legal Weapon was once described as "fast, funny and very powerful".

ISBN 1 902843 18 5

Cast: *2f & 2m with doubling*
Duration: *60 minutes approx.*
**KS 3 & 4 and A Level*

Legal Weapon II promises to be faster, funnier and far more powerful!

The Gate Escape by Mark Wheeller

The story of two truants. Corey is 'addicted' to bunking school. Chalkie views himself as a casual truant "no problem!" While truanting with some friends, the pair are greeted by a surreal 'Big Brother' figure who sets them a task. The loser will be in for some dramatic 'Big Bother'... Who will lose?... What will this 'bother' be?

The play has toured professionally in Hampshire in 2003, to great acclaim.

'A lively dramatic style and innovative structure with dynamic and contemporary dialogue. It is written in a way to guarantee that the audience will feel fully involved and enthralled by the main characters.'

Professor Ken Reid, Author of Tackling Truancy in Schools

ISBN 1 902843 14 2

Cast: *2f & 2m with doubling, or up to 30*
Duration: *70 minutes approx.*
KS 3 & 4

'I loved the piece – it really was Mark Wheeller at his absolute best... I loved so many of the ideas... inspired.'

Neil Phillips, Head of Drama and Edexcel GCSE Examiner

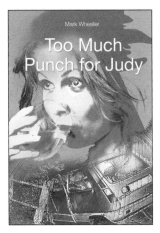

Too Much Punch for Judy by Mark Wheeller

A hard-hitting documentary play, based on a tragic drink-drive accident that results in the death of Jo, front seat passenger. The driver, her sister Judy, escapes unhurt (or has she?).

The tragic incident was dramatised by Mark in 1986 using only the words of those most closely involved and affected. This play has become one of the most frequently performed plays ever!

'The play will have an impact on young people or adults. It will provoke discussion. It stimulates and wants you to cry out for immediate social action and resolution.'

Henry Shankula – Addiction Research Foundation, Toronto

ISBN 1 902843 05 3

Cast: *2f & 2m with doubling or 3f, 3m & 6*
Duration: *50 minutes approx.*
KS 4 to adult

'The young audience I was sat in was patently out for some whooping Friday night fun... at the end there was a horrid silence.'

Nick Baker – Times Educational Supplement

Other plays published by *dbda*

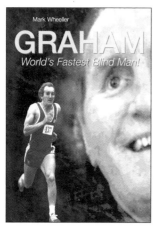

GRAHAM – World's Fastest Blind Man!
by Mark Wheeller

A play full of lively humour telling the inspirational story of Graham Salmon MBE. Totally blind since birth, Graham went on to become the World's Fastest Blind Man running 100 metres in 11.4 seconds! The play, written in Mark's unique documentary style, skillfully brings to life Graham's courage, tenacity and wonderful sense of humour.

'Very good, very moving, very very funny!'

Bruce Henderson, Principal Teacher of Drama, Wester Hailes Education Centre, Edinburgh

'I was really wowed by Graham... offered excellent opportunities for imaginative stylised performance with GCSE students... The peaks of tension and moments of pathos really moved me... I will definitely be offering Graham to my classes this year.'

Neil Phillips, Head of Drama and Edexcel GCSE Examiner

ISBN 1 902843 09 6

Cast: *5m & 4f with doubling, or up to 34*
Duration: *80 minutes approx.*
KS 3/4 to adult

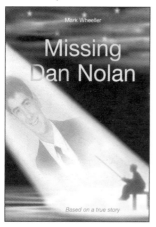

Missing Dan Nolan (based on a true story)
by Mark Wheeller

This play, based on the true story of Dan Nolan, a teenage boy who went missing on the night of January 1st 2002, is written in the same documentary style as 'Too Much Punch for Judy'. During 2003, it has been shown at various Drama Festivals and has won awards and commendations at every one!

'Unusual and deeply affecting. Skillfully written... achieves astonishing depth and authenticity... addresses a wound still raw and stands as a fitting testament to a young life.'

Charles Evans, Adjudicator, Eastleigh Drama Festival

ISBN 1 902843 16 9

Cast: *2m & 2f with doubling, or up to 18*
Duration: *45-50 minutes*
KS 3/4 to adult

Hard to Swallow by Mark Wheeller

This play is an adaptation of Maureen Dunbar's award winning book (and film) *Catherine* which charts her daughter's uneven battle with anorexia and the family's difficulties in coping with the illness.

The play has gone on to be performed all over the world to much acclaim, achieving considerable success in One Act Play Festivals. Its simple narrative style means that it is equally suitable for adult and older youth groups to perform.

'This play reaches moments of almost unbearable intensity... naturalistic scenes flow seamlessly into sequences of highly stylised theatre... such potent theatre!'

Vera Lustiq, The Independent

'Uncompromising and sensitive... should be compulsory viewing to anyone connected with the education of teenagers.'

Mick Martin, Times Educational Supplement

ISBN 1 902843 08 8

Cast: 3f & 2m with doubling, or 6f, 3m & 16
Duration: 70 minutes
KS 3 to adult

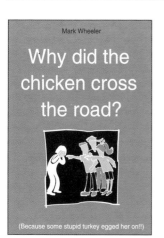

Why did the chicken cross the road? by Mark Wheeller

The story of two cousins, Tammy and Chris. Tammy gets killed in a stupid game of 'chicken' on the one morning that the cousins do not cycle to school. Chris, unable to tell anyone else about his part in the accident, has to live with this dreadful secret.

'An imaginative and moving look at risk taking at a time when peer pressure is at its strongest.'

Rosie Welch, LARSOA

ISBN 1 902843 00 2

Cast: 2m & 2f with doubling, or 3f, 3m & 3
Duration: 35 minutes
KS 3 & 4

Other plays published by *dbda*

Wacky Soap – *a Musical with a difference...*

Wacky Soap is a Pythonesque allegorical tale about 'substance' abuse (drugs, alcohol, glue, tobacco, etc). While washing with Wacky Soap leads to instant happiness and an inclination towards outrageous behaviour, prolonged use washes away limbs and ultimately leads to dematerialisation. This has become a tried and tested (and increasingly popular) School/ Drama Club/Youth Theatre production and is an ideal vehicle for a cast of any age.

The story of Wacky Soap, by Mark Wheeller, first appeared as a full **Musical play.** The play script of the full version (shown below) includes scheme of work for KS3/4. A mini version of the play is included with the **Music Score.**

ISBN 1 902843 02 9
KS 3/4 to adult

Wacky Soap – A Cautionary Tale by Mark Wheeller

Cast: 6-100!
Duration: 50 mins play / 80 mins musical

'This (play) gave every member of the large and energetic cast opportunities to shine... King Huff addressed his subjects from a Bouncy Castle, just one of the touches of visual humour in this fast, funny and thought provoking evening'.

Barbara Hart, Southern Evening Echo
Curtain Call Nominated "Best Production 2000"

ISBN 1 902843 06 1
KS 2&3

Wacky Soap – The Music Score and Mini Musical
by Mark Wheeller and James Holmes

Mini-Musical Duration: 40 mins

A **Past-performance CD** gives you the opportunity to hear the songs of the play, while a fully orchestrated **Backing track CD** will be invaluable to those who want to produce the play but do not have music facilities.

"Wacky Soap' was an outstanding success!!!... We have had letters from people in the audience saying what a fab show it was and how impressed they were.

The most frequent comment was that it was a 'risk' to put it on as a school show (as opposed to doing 'Oliver' or 'Little Shop of Horrors') and one that thoroughly paid off!! 'The feel good factor was amazing' was another comment we had.

Many people said how impressed they were by the 'community' spirit of the production – everybody working together without the 'star' element creeping in!"

John Plant, Head of Drama, Southmoor School, Sunderland

The Story of Wacky Soap
by Mark & Rachel Wheeller
Illustrations by Geoffrey Greiggs

ISBN 1 902843 07 X

A beautifully illustrated book with the story of Wacky Soap in prose form.
It is often used as inspiration with props and costumes for when producing the play.

Other plays by Wayne Denfhy

Published by Schoolplay Productions Ltd:

We'll be home tomorrow

Is it time yet Dad?

Postman's Knock (Musical with Chris Allen)

Published by Musicline Publications:

Handful of stars (Musical with Ken Meanwell)